THE COMMON WORM

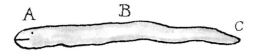

All good worms have a beginning, a
middle and an end.

Worms with two beginnings, a middle
and no end are apt to injure
themselves.

Worms with two ends, a middle and
no beginning get bored.

Deaf worms are not common.

Overweight worms are not common either.

Shy worms are hardly ever to be seen at all.

Worms in peril no. 14

The life of the common worm, though it may appear carefree, is not without its disadvantages.
The growth of football as a popular sport has added greatly to the problems of being a worm.

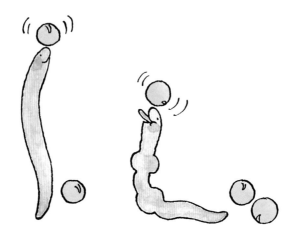

Worms balancing peas

The intelligence of the common worm is low. Nevertheless worms can learn to perform simple tricks and will, with the right sort of encouragement, fetch things.

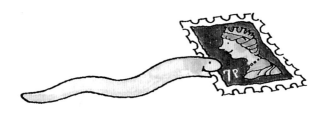

Young worm fetching a postage stamp for its master

YOU AND YOUR WORM

Pedigree worm   *Mongrel worm*

Worms make good pets. A worm is more loyal than a snail, more fun than a slug and less liable to fly away than a ladybird.

POINTS TO LOOK FOR WHEN BUYING WORMS

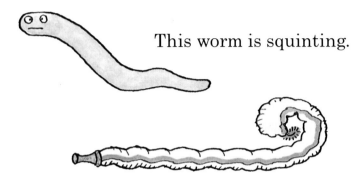

This worm is squinting.

This is not a worm, it is something else.

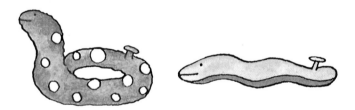

These may well be inflatable worms.

This worm has
a hat on.

A suitable disguise for the young worm hunter

When catching worms for yourself, the element of surprise is most important. Try not to let them know you are coming.

An unsuitable disguise

The Hollow Apple Trap

The Birtwhistle Suction Trap

Mirror Decoy

It is sometimes possible to ambush a worm. Traps also can give good results. Nets are not recommended. The lasso should be used sparingly, if at all.

Bad work with a lasso

Pet worms need lots of attention: appetizing food, comfortable quarters, the right amount of exercise.

A converted glove makes a cosy home

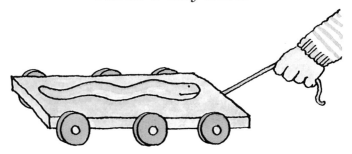

Exercising the growing worm

The worm, when properly cared for, can survive to an advanced age.

A useful bed for sick worms

To complete this chapter, here are the main health hazards of the worm with some suggested treatments.

A severe case of knots

The 'Little Wonder' worm collar prevents tail-biting

Lumps

Electric shock or lightning

Sunburn

How to catch a young worm for treatment

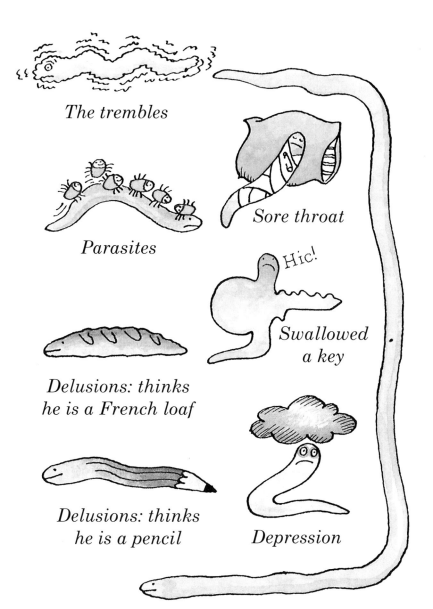

The trembles

Parasites

Sore throat

Hic!

Swallowed a key

Delusions: thinks he is a French loaf

Delusions: thinks he is a pencil

Depression

This worm may have outgrown his strength

WORMS AROUND THE WORLD

It is often said that worms in one country must be much like those in another. But this is not so.

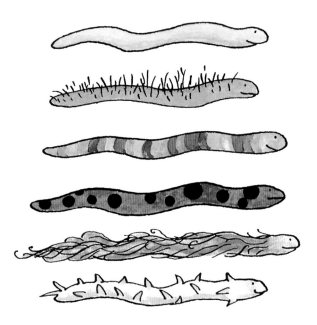

Syrian Big Worm

Borneo Dog Worm

The wild worms of the Pampas

The Fountain of Worms

In some parts of the world the worm is treated as a sacred animal. Statues and fountains are put up in his honour.

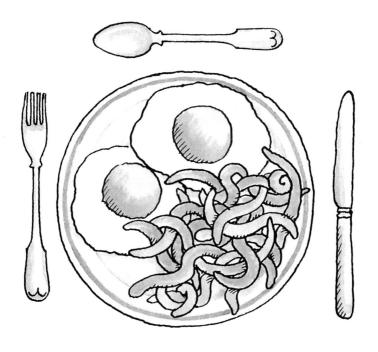

In other parts of the world the worm is treated as a sausage. Plates of worms are served with eggs, and the wormburger is a popular snack.

A SHORT HISTORY OF THE WORM

There have been worms on the Earth,
or rather in it, ever since time began.
When dinosaurs trampled noisily and
pushed each other around, the worms
were there keeping well out of the way.

Egyptian worms – sand worms, that is – observed the building of the Pyramids.

Chinese worms followed the construction of the Great Wall of China from start to finish.

Roman worms were in Rome before even the first brick was laid.

Worms were present at the battles of
Hastings, Agincourt, Borodino and
Bull Run.

Hastings

Agincourt

Borodino

Bull Run

When man's explorations took him to new lands, the worms were there waiting for him. American Indian worms saw Columbus arrive. African worms watched David Livingstone complete his epic journey to the Victoria Falls.

WORMS OF CHARACTER

1. MOUNTAIN RESCUE WORMS

In mountainous regions local worms are sometimes called upon to rescue the foolhardy visitor.

Leaping worm

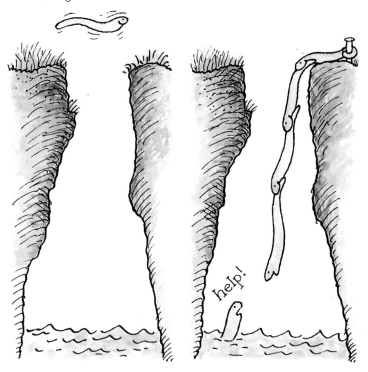

help!

Worms to the rescue

2. THE BERTRAM WORM CIRCUS

This circus tours three continents and is the only one of its kind in the world.

3. CLOCKWORK WORMS AND OTHER ODDITIES

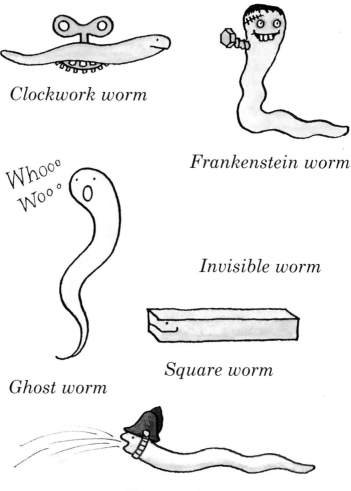

Clockwork worm

Frankenstein worm

Invisible worm

Ghost worm

Square worm

Fireman's worm

4. WORMS IN WARTIME

During the final stages of World War Two special teams of worms were trained to carry secret messages behind enemy lines.

WORMS TO COME

The future of the worm can only be guessed at. Already worms of exceptional character and intelligence have begun to emerge.

Worm disguised to fool passing bird

WORM INTELLIGENCE EXPERIMENT

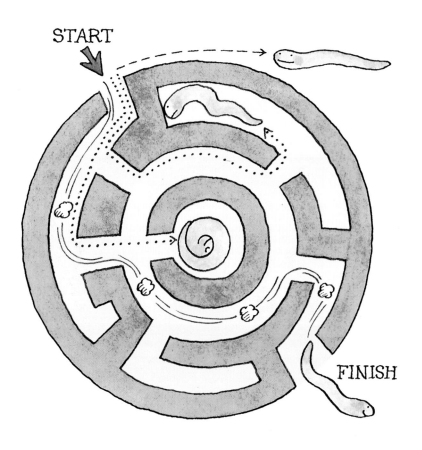

- – – – – – → *backward*
- · · · · · · · · · ·> *normal*
- =🐛 =🐛= *exceptional*

The worms were here before us. Perhaps, when we are gone, they will be here still – Lords of the Earth.

THE END